THE OFFICIAL MACCLESFIELD TOWN QUIZ BOOK

THE OFFICIAL MACCLESFIELD TOWN QUIZ BOOK

**Compiled by Chris Cowlin,
Kevin Snelgrove and John DT White**

Forewords by Mike Rance and Sammy McIlroy MBE

APEX PUBLISHING LTD

Hardback first published in 2009 by
Apex Publishing Ltd
PO Box 7086, Clacton on Sea, Essex, CO15 5WN, England
www.apexpublishing.co.uk

British Library Cataloguing-in-Publication Data
A catalogue record for this book
is available from the British Library

ISBN HARDBACK: 1-906358-42-7   978-1-906358-42-6

Typeset in 10.5pt Chianti Bdlt Win95BT

Cover Design: Siobhan Smith

Printed and bound in Great Britain by
the MPG Books Group, Bodmin and King's Lynn

Author's Note:
Please can you contact me: **ChrisCowlin@btconnect.com** if you find any
mistakes/errors in this book as I would like to put them right on any
future reprints of this book. I would also like to hear from Macclesfield
Town fans who have enjoyed the test! For more information on me and
my books please look at: **www.ChrisCowlin.com**

This book is an official product of Macclesfield Town Football Club

We would like to dedicate this book to:

All the players and staff who have worked for the club during their history.

FOREWORD

In the mid 90s Macclesfield Town was the most successful football club in the non-league pyramid. Sammy McIlroy built on a platform created by his predecessor Peter Wragg to lead the club to two GM Vauxhall Conference titles in 1995 and 1997 and an FA Trophy win at Wembley in 1996. The second of the two Conference titles resulted in the realisation of the late Arthur Jones' vision of the Silkmen playing in the Football League and twelve months later the Silkmen were playing League games at Maine Road, Deepdale and the Britannia Stadium. We were living the dream.

As I write these notes the club has just completed its 12th season as a member of that August competition, a tremendous achievement for a small club that lives in the shadow of many more illustrious neighbours. But the Silkmen have a long and proud history that stretches back to 1874, a history that has had its fair share of triumphs and disappointments but has always been marked by the commitment and support of the community for its local football team.

In the pubs and bars of Macclesfield and in the virtual world of the internet message boards, supporters often test their knowledge of the team they love. Many are encyclopaedic in grasp of the history of the team and the charismatic individuals who have contributed over the years to the unfolding saga.

This book compiled by Chris Cowlin and his colleagues, aided and abetted by Geoff Knights, will bring an extra dimension to those debates and arguments. It's a quiz book with depth and it's focused directly at the Silkmen and the men who've made history at the Moss Rose. Test yourself on your knowledge of Macclesfield Town and enjoy!

Best wishes
Mike Rance

FOREWORD

My time spent at Macclesfield Town was very special, not only for the success and trophies we won, but also the great players that worked under Gil Prescott and I.

The spirit at the club was fantastic! We took that onto the field of play and the terraces. I must mention Arthur Jones who backed me in everyway as a chairman and friend, without his support we would not be a League club today.

The loyal fans of Macclesfield will surely enjoy using this book and of course with that a lot of memories will come to mind.

Best wishes
Sammy McIlroy MBE

INTRODUCTION

I would first of all like to thank Mike Rance and Sammy McIlroy MBE for writing the forewords to this book. I am very grateful to them for their help and support on this project.

I would also like to thank all the past and present staff of Macclesfield Town Football Club, all the newspapers and radio stations for their comments and reviews on this book (these can be found at the back of the book).

I would also like to thank Patrick Nelson at Macclesfield Town Football Club and Geoffrey Knights (the club's modern-day historian and statistician) for their help during the books compilation.

I hope you enjoy this book. Hopefully it should bring back some wonderful memories!

It was great working with Kevin Snelgrove and John DT White again, we have written over 60 books between us. We have given you a selection of easy, medium and hard questions.

In closing, I would like to thank all my friends and family for encouraging me to complete this book.

Chris Cowlin

Best wishes
Chris Cowlin

Visit Chris Cowlin's website:

www.ChrisCowlin.com

Visit Kevin Snelgrove's website:

www.KevinSnelgrove.co.uk

CLUB HISTORY & RECORDS

1. *In what year were Macclesfield formed?*

2. *What is the name of Macclesfield Town's ground?*

3. *Which player scored 83 League and Cup goals in the season of 1933/34?*

4. *In which season did Macclesfield Town enter the Football League?*

5. *In what year did Macclesfield add 'Town' to their name?*

6. *Which player holds the club record of 610 (62) League and non-League appearances for Macclesfield Town?*

7. *Which Macclesfield Town player scored the final goal of the last millennium?*

8. *On 1 September 1965 Macclesfield Town first played at home under floodlights, winning 4-1 against which opponents?*

9. *What is Macclesfield Town's nickname?*

10. *Following on from question 4, who were Macclesfield Town's first ever opponents at home in the Football League on 9 August, Macclesfield winning 2-1 with goals from Efe Sodje and Richard Landon?*

ALAN NAVARRO

11. At what Lancashire club did Alan begin his career in 2000, although he never played for their first team?

12. Following on from the previous question, Alan was sent on loan from this club in 2001 to which club with an 'x' in their name?

13. In what year did Alan arrive at Macclesfield Town on loan?

14. Name the 'Rovers' that Alan signed in November 2001.

15. To the nearest 10, how many League appearances did Alan make during his two spells with the club?

16. How many goals did Alan score for Macclesfield – 3, 6 or 9?

17. In what year did Alan leave Macclesfield Town?

18. Following on from the previous question, what team did Alan join on leaving Macclesfield?

19. Alan played 3 League games for which then non-League club in 2005?

20. Who managed Alan at both Macclesfield Town and the club in question 18?

CLUB HONOURS

*Match up the honour achieved by Macclesfield Town
with the correct year*

21.	FA Challenge Trophy winners (1st time)	1997
22.	Bob Lord Trophy winners	1891
23.	Combination runners-up for the 1st time	1998
24.	Cheshire Senior Cup winners (20th time)	1970
25.	GM Vauxhall Conference champions (2nd time)	1932
26.	Northern Premier League champions (1st time)	2000
27.	Cheshire County League champions (1st time)	2005
28.	Third Division runners-up	1987
29.	Northern Premier League Challenge Cup winners	1969
30.	League Two play-off semi-finalists	1994

THE LEAGUE CUP

31. Name the 'United' that knocked Macclesfield Town out of the 2004/05 League Cup.

32. In season 2002/03 Macclesfield lost in the League Cup to the team that won the first ever domestic Double in English football. Name them.

33. Can you name the 2008 FA Cup runners-up that put Macclesfield out of the League Cup in season 2005/06?

34. In season 1997/98 which club, who played in the Premiership in season 2008/09 for the first time in their history, ended Macclesfield's League Cup hopes?

35. Macclesfield went out of the 1998/99 League Cup having lost their round 2 tie 9-0 on aggregate. Can you name the 'City' that defeated them?

36. Which 2004 League Cup winners ended Macclesfield's League Cup dreams in 2000/01?

37. Name the Yorkshire 'United' that put Macclesfield out of the 2003/04 League Cup.

38. Which League Cup winners in 1997 and 2000 ended Macclesfield's League Cup hopes in season 2006/07?

39. Name the former Premier League 'United' that beat Macclesfield in the 2007/08 League Cup.

40. Can you name the Yorkshire 'City' that beat Town in the 2001/02 League Cup in round 1?

WHERE DID THEY GO? – 1

Match up the player with the club he joined on leaving Macclesfield Town

41.	Carl Regan	Dundalk
42.	Paul Harsley	Albion Rovers
43.	John Miles	Rhyl Town
44.	Alan Fettis	MK Dons
45.	Neil Howarth	Bury
46.	Robbie Doyle	Valletta
47.	John Coleman	Accrington Stanley
48.	Lee Martin	Port Vale
49.	Luke Dimech	Huddersfield Town
50.	Martin Clark	Cheltenham Town

DANNY SWAILES

51. In which year was Danny born – 1979, 1980 or 1981?

52. From which team did Macclesfield Town sign Danny in January 2005?

53. Against which team did Danny make his Macclesfield debut in a 2-0 home win during January 2005?

54. Against which team did Danny score his first Macclesfield League goal in a 3-0 home win during January 2006?

55. How many League goals did Danny score for Macclesfield during 2005/06?

56. In which position does Danny play – defender, midfielder or striker?

57. In what year did Danny leave Macclesfield Town?

58. Following on from the previous question, which team did Danny join when he left the club?

59. How many League goals did Danny score during his Macclesfield Town career – 3, 5 or 7?

60. Against which team did Danny score the winning goal in a 2-1 League home win during December 2006?

FOOTBALL LEAGUE MANAGERS

Match up the manager with the period they were in charge at Macclesfield Town

61.	Sammy McIlroy	2008-09
62.	Peter Davenport	2007-08
63.	Brian Horton	2001
64.	Paul Ince	2000
65.	Kevin Keen	1993-2000
66.	John Askey	2001
67.	Ian Brightwell	2004-06
68.	Gil Prescott	2006-07
69.	David Moss	2003-04
70.	Keith Alexander	2001-03

2008/2009

71.   Name the Premier League side that knocked
        Macclesfield out of the 2008/09 Carling Cup.

72.   Which 'Town' beat Macclesfield 4-0 on the opening
        day of the season?

73.   Against which side did The Silkmen record their first
        League win of the campaign?

74.   Can you name the non-League 'Town' that The Silkmen
        beat 2-0 away in the FA Cup?

75.   Who scored Macclesfield's first goal of the season?

76.   Macclesfield lost 4-1 at which coastal club on Boxing
        Day 2008?

77.   In what competition did Macclesfield lose 3-0 away to
        Crewe Alexandra?

78.   Can you name the seaside club that Macclesfield beat
        in round 1 of the League Cup?

79.   Who scored Macclesfield's first League goal of the
        season?

80.   Name the 1995 FA Cup winners that knocked
        Macclesfield out of the FA Cup.

NATIONALITIES – 1

Match up the player with his nationality

81.	Kyle Lightbourne	Nigerian
82.	Tony Williams	Maltese
83.	Patrece Liburd	English
84.	James McNulty	Dutch Colony Surinam
85.	David Morley	Bermudian
86.	Fola Onibuje	Irish
87.	Luke Dimech	English
88.	Robbie Doyle	Kittitian & Nevisian
89.	Karl Munroe	Welsh
90.	Clyde Wijnhard	English

2007/2008

91. **Can you name the 'County' that put The Silkmen out of the Johnstone's Paint Trophy?**

92. **With which former Premier League club did Macclesfield draw 1-1 away in their opening League game?**

93. **Which 'colourful' player scored Macclesfield's opening League goal of the campaign?**

94. **Against which Greater Manchester club did Macclesfield suffer their final defeat of the season?**

95. **On Boxing Day 2007 Macclesfield lost 1-0 at which 'United'?**

96. **Name the striker who scored Macclesfield's last goal of 2007.**

97. **On New Year's Day The Silkmen lost 3-0 away to a team that in 1961 lost the inaugural League Cup final to Aston Villa. Name them.**

98. **Name the last team that Macclesfield beat in the League this season.**

99. **Michael Husbands scored the winner for Macclesfield against which Welsh side in The Football League Trophy?**

100. **Against which 'United' did The Silkmen record their first League win of the campaign?**

WHERE DID THEY COME FROM? – 1

Match up the player with the club he left to join Macclesfield Town

101.	Neil Harvey	Swindon Town
102.	Richard Irving	Northampton Town
103.	Kevin McIntyre	Nottingham Forest
104.	David Flitcroft	Burnley
105.	Michael Husbands	Retford United
106.	Neil Moore	Worcester City
107.	Richard Edghill	Rochdale
108.	Paul Ince	Port Vale
109.	Terry Dunfield	Chester City
110.	Harry Lovatt	Bradford City

PAUL INCE – 1

111.   Can you name the Italian Serie A side that Paul played for during his career?

112.   Following on from the previous question, which English side did Paul join when he returned home from Italy?

113.   In what year was Paul appointed as boss of The Silkmen?

114.   Can you recall Paul's nickname during his playing days?

115.   In 2002 Paul signed for which Midlands side?

116.   For which club did Paul make the most appearances during his career?

117.   What was the first winners' medal that Paul won during his professional playing career?

118.   Name the 'Town' that Paul played for in 2006.

119.   Paul once managed a team that had previously won the Premier League. Name them.

120.   How many Premier League winners' medals did Paul win?

LEAGUE POSITIONS

Match up the season/points with Macclesfield Town's finishing position in the League

121.	2007/08, 50 points	5th
122.	1997/98, 82 points	20th
123.	2002/03, 54 points	13th
124.	1999/2000, 65 points	17th
125.	2006/07, 48 points	2nd
126.	2003/04, 52 points	14th
127.	1998/99, 43 points	16th
128.	2004/05, 75 points	24th
129.	2000/01, 56 points	19th
130.	2005/06, 54 points	22nd

DAVID FLITCROFT

131. David's older brother played for Manchester City and Blackburn Rovers. Name him.

132. At which Lancashire club did David begin his professional career, making 8 League appearances for them from 1992-93 and scoring 2 League goals?

133. Following on from question 131, to which 'City' was David sent on loan in 1993 from this club?

134. Can you name the team that David signed for in 1993, playing for them until 1999?

135. In 1999 David joined which team, helping them to the Division Three play-offs in season 2001/02?

136. Name the Greater Manchester side that David joined in 2004.

137. Can you name the town in Greater Manchester where David was born, the home of a Premier League club in season 2008/09?

138. In 2006 David joined which non-League 'United' in Greater Manchester?

139. Midway through the 2006/07 season David returned to which one of his old clubs as Keith Hill's assistant manager?

140. For which club did David play the most League games during his career?

KEITH ALEXANDER

141. Keith was born on 14 November 1956 in which Midlands city?

142. At which club did Keith start his professional career in 1974?

143. Which honour did Keith win with non-League Stamford at Wembley in 1980?

144. Keith transferred from Stockport County to Lincoln City in December 1990, for what transfer fee – £4,000, £7,000 or £10,000?

145. For which club did Keith make 83 League appearances and score 26 League goals (1988-90), the most in his League playing career?

146. In what position did Keith play in his playing days?

147. Which Macclesfield Town manager did Keith replace in February 2008?

148. In May 2006, at which club did Keith replace Steve Bleasdale as manager?

149. At which club has Keith had two spells as manager, 1993-94 and 2002-06, and one as assistant manager, 2001-02?

150. Keith has played at international level and made three appearances in 1990, for which country?

DEREK PARLANE

151. At which Scottish club did Derek begin his professional playing career in 1970?

152. In what year during the late 1980s did Derek sign for The Silkmen?

153. Can you name the Yorkshire side that Derek joined in 1980 after he left the club in question 151?

154. In 1983 Derek signed for which Lancashire 'City'?

155. Following on from the previous question, can you name this club's manager, who had captained Glasgow Celtic to European Cup glory in 1967?

156. Derek scored against which London club on his debut for the team in question 154 in the Second Division?

157. In season 1985/86 Derek played for Racing Jet, a team from which European country?

158. To which Welsh side was Derek sold in 1985?

159. Name the sportswear manufacturer that Derek was working for in 2009 and which have a Premier League club named them.

160. Can you name the Scottish club that Derek left to join Macclesfield?

SQUAD NUMBERS 2008/09 – 1

Match up the player with his squad number for the season

161.	Simon Yeo	25
162.	Chris Hirst	9
163.	Jonny Brain	10
164.	John Rooney	7
165.	Richard Walker	19
166.	Lee Bell	14
167.	Terry Dunfield	1
168.	James Jennings	3
169.	Ahmed Deen	21
170.	Martin Gritton	5

2006/2007

171. How many League games did it take for The Silkmen to record their first League win of the season – 14, 17 or 20?

172. Which side defeated Macclesfield on the opening day of the season?

173. Which 'County' knocked Macclesfield out of The Johnstone's Paint Trophy?

174. Can you name the midfielder that scored Macclesfield's first goal of the season?

175. On New Year's Day 2007 Macclesfield beat which 'City' 2-1 in the League?

176. Which team was the last side to defeat Macclesfield this season?

177. Which former Manchester City striker scored his first goal of the season in a 3-3 home draw at Torquay United?

178. Following on from question 171, name the Macclesfield striker that scored the only goal of this game against Rochdale.

179. Which striker scored Macclesfield's last goal of this season's campaign?

180. On Boxing Day 2006 The Silkmen beat which 'City' 3-0 away in the League?

WHERE DID THEY GO? – 2

*Match up the player with the club he joined
on leaving Macclesfield Town*

181.	Tommy Lee	Wycombe Wanderers
182.	Martin Carruthers	Witton Albion
183.	Tony Bullock	Chesterfield
184.	Tony Barras	Stockport County
185.	Colin Little	Hucknall Town
186.	Michael Carr	Lincoln City
187.	Chris Bettney	Halifax Town
188.	Matty McNeil	Boston United
189.	Martin Bullock	Worksop Town
190.	Michael Briscoe	Northwich Victoria

NEIL HOWARTH

191. Name the manager who was in charge of The Silkmen when Neil made his debut.

192. In which Lancashire town was Steve born – Blackburn, Bury or Farnworth?

193. To how many Conference titles did Neil lead Macclesfield Town?

194. In what season did Neil win his first Conference title with Macclesfield Town?

195. Can you recall the year in which Neil left The Silkmen?

196. Name the 'Town' that Neil joined when he left Macclesfield.

197. Following on from the previous question, how much did Neil cost his new club - £4,000, £7,000 or £10,000?

198. In which season did Neil captain The Silkmen to the runners-up spot in Division Three?

199. In 2003 Neil signed for which 'United'?

200. Neil was appointed as assistant manager of which club in January 2006?

WHERE DID THEY COME FROM? – 2

Match up the player with the club he left to join Macclesfield Town

201.	Peter Jackson	Bury
202.	Jamie Milligan	Swansea City
203.	Lee Clover	Hyde United
204.	Simon Collins	Luton Town
205.	Derek Kevan	Rotherham United
206.	Paul Morgan	Blackpool
207.	Jonny Brain	Stockport County
208.	Neil MacKenzie	Plymouth Argyle
209.	Simon Davies	Mansfield Town
210.	Karl Munroe	Port Vale

SIMON YEO

211.   Can you name the Greater Manchester "United" Simon
        scored 77 League goals for in 130 games between
        1998-2002?

212.   What is Simon's middle name – John, James or Jason?

213.   In what year did Simon join Macclesfield Town?

214.   Following on from the previous question, which
        Macclesfield manager signed Simon for the club?

215.   For which team did Simon play from 2002-05 and then
        again in 2006?

216.   In what position does Simon play?

217.   In which year was Simon born in Stockport – 1971,
        1972 or 1973?

218.   Against which team did Simon score a brace in a 4-1
        away League win during September 2008?

219.   Against which team did Simon score Macclesfield's
        goal in a 1-1 home League draw during February
        2009?

220.   Against which team did Simon score a League goal for
        Macclesfield in a 2-1 home win during September
        2009?

SQUAD NUMBERS 2008/09 – 2

Match up the player with his squad number for the season

221.	Danny Thomas	26
222.	Izak Reid	4
223.	Matthew Towns	12
224.	Francis Green	20
225.	Sean Hessey	13
226.	Neil Harvey	2
227.	Jamie Tolley	16
228.	Gareth Evans	11
229.	Shaun Brisley	15
230.	Nick Blackman	8

JOHN ASKEY

231.   In what positions did John play during his playing days?

232.   In what year did John sign permanently for Macclesfield Town - 1987, 1988 or 1989?

233.   How many Football League goals did John score in his Macclesfield career – 29, 30 or 31?

234.   Against which team did John score the only goal in a 1-0 away League win during March 2002?

235.   Against which team did John score in a 3-2 home League win during May 2003, his very last match for the club?

236.   In which year was John born in Stoke – 1962, 1963 or 1964?

237.   How many League goals did John score for Macclesfield Town during 2000/01?

238.   Against which team did John score Macclesfield's second goal in a 3-0 home League win during August 1997?

239.   How many yellow cards did John pick up while playing for Macclesfield during 1997/98 – 4, 8 or 12?

240.   How many Football League games did John play for Macclesfield in his career – 181, 191 or 201?

NATIONALITIES – 2

Match up the player with his nationality

241.	Matthew Tipton	Canadian
242.	Joaquin Medinilla-Cobotti	Welsh
243.	Martin Gritton	Herzegovian
244.	Ahmed Deen	English
245.	Dean Delaney	American
246.	Asmir Begovic	Scottish
247.	Boaz Myhill	Barbadian
248.	Terry Dunfield	Spanish
249.	Alan Navarro	Sierra Leonean
250.	Neil Harvey	Irish

1990s

251.   Name the team that Macclesfield beat 1-0 on New Year's Day 1990.

252.   The Silkmen lost to which Welsh side 1-0 at home but beat them 2-0 away in season 1990/91?

253.   In season 1991/92 Macclesfield played five teams named 'Town'. Can you name three of them?

254.   Which team did The Silkmen beat 3-2 in a penalty shootout in the third round of the FA Cup in season 1992/93?

255.   On the opening day of the 1993/94 season Macclesfield lost 5-1 away at which 'City'?

256.   Macclesfield beat which 'Rovers' 4-0 at home in their final League game of the 1996/97 season?

257.   The Silkmen drew their last three League games of the 1995/96 season 1-1. Name any one of their three opponents.

258.   Can you name the 'City' that knocked The Silkmen out of the League Cup in season 1997/98?

259.   In season 1998/99 Macclesfield lost both their League games to the team that won the European Cup Winners' Cup in 1970. Can you name them?

260.   Name the 'United' that Macclesfield beat 2-1 in their final game of the decade.

FA CUP WINS

Match up the season/round with the FA Cup winning result

261. 1972/73, 2nd qualifying round   **MT 4-2 Carlisle United**

262. 1997/98, 1st round   **MT 2-0 Spennymoor United**

263. 2006/07, 2nd round   **MT 3-0 Glossop**

264. 1987/88, 2nd round   **Mexborough Town 1-2 MT**

265. 1982/83, 4th qualifying round   **MT 4-1 Cambridge United**

266. 1967/68, 2nd round   **MT 2-1 Hartlepool United**

267. 1998/99, 2nd round   **MT 3-1 Stafford Rangers**

268. 2001/02, 2nd round   **Hartlepool United 2-4 MT**

269. 1987/88, 1st round   **MT 4-1 Swansea City**

270. 1975/76, 4th qualifying round   **MT 4-0 Rotherham United**

2005/2006

271. The Silkmen lost 2-1 away to which London club on the opening day of the season?

272. Name the former European Cup winners that Macclesfield knocked out of the League Cup.

273. Can you name the midfielder that scored The Silkmen's opening goal of the season?

274. Name any one of the three 'Uniteds' that Macclesfield beat in The Football League Trophy.

275. Macclesfield defeated which 'County' 6-0 on Boxing Day 2005?

276. Name the 'Rovers' that Macclesfield beat 3-2 away on the final day of the season.

277. Following on from the previous question, name the on-loan striker who scored Macclesfield's 89th-minute winner and secured their League safety.

278. On 2 January 2006 The Silkmen won a dramatic game 5-4 away to which 'Wanderers'?

279. Which 'City' knocked Macclesfield out of the League Cup?

280. Name the team that knocked The Silkmen out of The Football League Trophy on the away goals rule.

TOP FOOTBALL LEAGUE APPEARANCES

Match the player with the number of appearances he made for Macclesfield Town

281.	Danny Whitaker	181
282.	Steve Hitchen	134
283.	Darren Tinson	114
284.	Kevin McIntyre	171
285.	Michael Welsh	148
286.	Matthew Tipton	263
287.	John Askey	151
288.	Chris Priest	164
289.	Danny Adams	134
290.	Steve Wilson	150

2004/2005

291. Who scored Macclesfield's opening goal of the season in a 3-1 home victory over Leyton Orient?

292. Which 'United' knocked The Silkmen out of the League Cup?

293. Which 'Town' did The Silkmen beat 4-0 in the LDV Vans Trophy?

294. Name the non-League 'Town' that The Silkmen beat 2-0 in an FA Cup replay.

295. Which team did The Silkmen beat 1-0 on the final day of the League season to book a place in the League Two play-off semi-finals?

296. Macclesfield's best win of the season was a 5-0 away victory. Who did they beat?

297. Which club defeated Macclesfield in the League Two play-offs?

298. Following on from the previous question, who scored for Macclesfield in their 2-1 two-leg defeat?

299. Can you name the 'City' that ended The Silkmen's FA Cup dreams?

300. Which 'Rovers' knocked The Silkmen out of The LDV Vans Trophy?

EFE SODJE

301. Efe was born in Greenwich on 5 October of which year
     – 1972, 1974 or 1976?

302. In what position does Efe play?

303. Efe scored on his League debut in 1997 for which club?

304. Efe has featured at international level in the 2000
     African Cup of Nations and the 2002 FIFA World Cup
     for which country?

305. How many League appearances did Efe make for
     Macclesfield Town – 83, 93 or 103?

306. Efe's playing career started in 1994 at Stevenage
     Borough, where he made how many League
     appearances before moving to Macclesfield Town – 35,
     40 or 45?

307. Efe is famous for wearing something that bears the
     words 'Against all odds'. What is it?

308. How many League goals did Efe score for The Silkmen
     – 3, 6 or 9?

309. In 1999 Efe left Macclesfield Town to join which club?

310. In 2008 Efe joined which Lancashire club after a loan
     spell?

DANNY THOMAS

311.   In what position does Danny play?

312.   In which year was Danny born in Leamington Spa –
       1980, 1981 or 1982?

313.   For which team did Danny play before joining
       Macclesfield Town in 2007?

314.   Against which team did Danny score a brace in a 4-1
       home League win during October 2008?

315.   True or false: Danny scored a League hat-trick for
       Macclesfield during 2007/08?

316.   Against which team did Danny make his Macclesfield
       Town League debut during August 2007 in a 1-1 away
       draw?

317.   Which Macclesfield Town manager signed Danny for
       the club?

318.   For which team did Danny play between 2004 and
       2006?

319.   Can you name the former European Cup winners
       where Danny began his professional playing career in
       1997 although he failed to make their first team?

320.   What is Danny's middle name – Jeremy, Jonathan or
       Justin?

BRIAN HORTON

321. In which Staffordshire town was Brian born in February 1949 – Biddulph, Hednesford or Lichfield?

322. At which club did Brian start his professional playing career in 1970?

323. What fee did Brighton & Hove Albion pay Port Vale for Brian in 1976 - £20,000, £25,000 or £30,000?

324. Brian was playing for which club when they escaped relegation on the last day of the season in 1983, resulting in their opponents Manchester City being relegated to Division Two?

325. Which club did Brian leave to become manager of Macclesfield Town in April 2004?

326. Of the 131 games played while Brian was in charge of Macclesfield Town, how many did The Silkmen win – 47, 57 or 67?

327. Which award did Brian win in February 2005?

328. Brian went on to manage three of the four League clubs he was with as a player. Can you name all three?

329. Which manager did Brian succeed at Macclesfield Town in 2004?

330. During his 16-year playing career, how many League appearances did Brian make – 684, 784 or 884?

SEAN HESSEY

331. In what position does Sean play?

332. Name the Yorkshire "Town" which Sean played for in season 1998-99.

333. What is Sean's middle name – Peter, Paul or Philip?

334. From which club did Macclesfield Town sign Sean in 2008, after a loan spell during 2007/08?

335. For which Scottish club did Sean play between 1999 and 2004?

336. Which manager signed Sean on loan for Macclesfield during November 2007?

337. Which manager signed Sean on a permanent basis for Macclesfield Town during June 2008?

338. True or false: while on loan at Macclesfield Town during 2007/08 Sean scored two League goals for the club?

339. What nationality is Sean?

340. In what year was Sean born –1978, 1979 or 1980?

PLAYING YEARS AT THE CLUB – 1

Match up the player with the period he spent at Macclesfield Town

341.	George Abbey	1893-94
342.	Mike Lake	2005-07
343.	Albert Valentine	1999-2004
344.	Rae Ingram (second spell)	1958-59
345.	Martin Bullock	1989
346.	Tony Waiters	1986-89
347.	David Flitcroft	1933-34
348.	Neil Mitchell	2003-04
349.	Joe Rogers	1996-98
350.	John Butcher	1998-2001

351. If The Silkmen visited The City of Manchester Stadium, what team would they be playing away?

352. If The Silkmen visited Walker's Stadium, what team would they be playing away?

353. If The Silkmen visited Victoria Park, what 'United' would they be playing away?

354. If The Silkmen visited Sincil Bank, what 'City' would they be playing away?

355. If The Silkmen visited Stonebridge Road, what team would they be playing away?

356. If The Silkmen visited the Stadium of Light, what team would they be playing away?

357. If The Silkmen visited Kenilworth Road, what 'Town' would they be playing away?

358. If The Silkmen visited Galpharm Stadium, what team would they be playing away?

359. If The Silkmen visited The Hawthorns, what Midlands club would they be playing away?

360. If The Silkmen visited The Shay Stadium, what 'Town' would they be playing away?

MATCH THE YEAR – 1

Match up the event with the year it took place

361. The Silkmen played their 500th
     consecutive League game against
     Barnet at Moss Rose   1911

362. Macclesfield Town became founder
     members of the Northern Premier League   1970

363. Macclesfield played in the FA Cup first
     round proper for the first time   1994

364. Macclesfield joined The Cheshire League   1884

365. The Silkmen won the inaugural FA
     Trophy final by beating Telford 2-0   2008

366. Macclesfield last shared a Division
     with local rivals Altrincham   1946

367. Macclesfield won the Staffordshire
     Senior Cup   1932

368. Macclesfield Town became the
     Manchester League champions for
     the second time   1968

369. The Silkmen recorded their biggest
     FA Cup win of 9-0 against Hartford
     St. John's   1996

370. Macclesfield Town won the Cheshire
     League and the Cheshire League
     Challenge Cup Double   1960

JAMIE TOLLEY

371. From which club did Jamie sign to join Macclesfield Town in 2006?

372. Following on from the previous question, Jamie became this club's youngest ever player, at what age?

373. For which country did Jamie win 12 Under-21 caps and score 1 goal during his career?

374. In which position does Jamie play – defender, midfielder or striker?

375. Name the "Town" where Jamie went on trial during the summer of 2007-08 before deciding to return to The Silkmen.

376. Which Macclesfield Town manager signed Jamie for the club?

377. Against which team did Jamie make his Macclesfield Town debut during August 2006 in a 2-1 home defeat?

378. Against which team did Jamie score his first Macclesfield League goal in a 3-3 home draw during December 2006?

379. Against which team was Jamie sent off during a 3-0 away win on Boxing Day 2006?

380. In which year was Jamie born in Ludlow – 1983, 1984 or 1985?

CAPS FOR MY COUNTRY

Match up the player with the number of caps he
won for his country

381.	Kyle Lightbourne	38 Canada caps
382.	Andrejus Tereskinas	14 England caps
383.	Paul Ince	1 Wales cap
384.	Luke Dimech	56 Lithuania caps
385.	Keith Alexander	60 Malta caps
386.	Neil Harvey	12 Scotland caps
387.	Derek Kevan	53 England caps
388.	Martin Nash	40 Bermuda caps
389.	Simon Davies	3 Barbados caps
390.	Derek Parlane	3 St Lucia caps

391.   If The Silkmen were in opposition against The Tangerines, what team would they be playing?

392.   If The Silkmen were in opposition against The Stags, what 'Town' would they be playing?

393.   If The Silkmen were in opposition against The Daggers, what team would they be playing?

394.   If The Silkmen were in opposition against The Tykes, what team would they be playing?

395.   If The Silkmen were in opposition against The Bees, can you name one of the two teams they could be playing?

396.   If The Silkmen were in opposition against The Pilgrims, what team would they be playing?

397.   If The Silkmen were in opposition against The Bluebirds, what team would they be playing?

398.   If The Silkmen were in opposition against The Stanley, what team would they be playing?

399.   If The Silkmen were in opposition against The Pirates, what team would they be playing?

400.   If The Silkmen were in opposition against The Brewers, what 'Albion' would they be playing?

MATCH THE YEAR – 2

Match up the event with the year it took place

401.	John Coleman was born	2003
402.	Macclesfield moved from Victoria Road to Moss Rose	1979
403.	Sammy McIlroy was appointed manager of Macclesfield Town	1955
404.	Macclesfield Town finished bottom of the Northern Premier League	1891
405.	Darren Tinson scored his first League goal in his 127th League appearance for The Silkmen	1998
406.	Joe Rogers sadly passed away	2007
407.	Ryan Price made his 100th League appearances for The Silkmen	1993
408.	Martin Gritton signed for Macclesfield Town from Lincoln City	1962
409.	Boaz Myhill joined The Silkmen on a three-month loan	1999
410.	Richard Irving left Macclesfield after playing only 9 League matches for the club and retired from the professional game	2000

AWAY DAYS – 2

411. **If The Silkmen visited St Andrew's, what team would they be playing away?**

412. **If The Silkmen visited Ninian Park, what 'City' would they be playing away?**

413. **If The Silkmen visited Sixfields, what 'Town' would they be playing away?**

414. **If The Silkmen visited The Memorial Ground, what 'Rovers' would they be playing away?**

415. **If The Silkmen visited Moss Lane, what team would they be playing away?**

416. **If The Silkmen visited Ewood Park, what team would they be playing away?**

417. **If The Silkmen visited The Ricoh Arena, what 'City' would they be playing away?**

418. **If The Silkmen visited Abbey Stadium, what 'United' would they be playing away?**

419. **If The Silkmen visited Gigg Lane, what team would they be playing away?**

420. **If The Silkmen visited Pirelli Stadium, what 'Albion' would they be playing away?**

JON PARKIN

421. Where in South Yorkshire was Jon born on 30 December 1981 – Doncaster, Rotherham or Barnsley?

422. What was Jon's nickname at Macclesfield?

423. How many League appearances did Jon make for Macclesfield Town – 63 (2), 73 (2) or 83 (2)?

424. From which club did Jon join Macclesfield Town in February 2004?

425. In season 2004/05 Jon made 44 League appearances for The Silkmen, scoring how many League goals?

426. In June 2007 Jon moved from Hull City to Stoke City, for what transfer fee - £170,000, £270,000 or £370,000?

427. How many League goals did Jon score during his two years at Macclesfield Town – 20, 25 or 30?

428. At which club did Jon start his professional playing career in 1998?

429. Jon made his debut for which club on 1 September 2008 in a home 2-1 win over Charlton Athletic?

430. Jon was a striker but while at York City (2002-04) he also played in another position – which one?

PAUL INCE – 2

431. From whom did Paul take over as Macclesfield manager in October 2006?

432. True or false: Paul's first managerial role was as Macclesfield Town manager?

433. When Paul left the club as manager, which team did he go on to manage?

434. In what position did Paul play during his playing days?

435. True or false: Paul played a League match for Macclesfield Town during his career?

436. At which London club did Paul start his playing career in the mid-1980s?

437. How many goals did Paul score while achieving his 53 full international caps – 2, 4 or 6?

438. True or false: Paul won his first match in charge of Macclesfield Town during October 2006 against Mansfield at home in the League?

439. Against which team did Macclesfield record their first win with Paul as manager, in a 1-0 FA Cup 1st round replay during November 2006?

440. Who took over from Paul as Macclesfield Town manager during June 2007?

TRANSFERS

Match up the player with the transfer fee paid by Macclesfield Town

441.	Kevin Keen from Stoke City (2000)	£30,000
442.	Ben Sedgemore from Mansfield Town (1998)	£10,000
443.	Pat Connolly from Crewe Alexandra (1962)	£40,000
444.	Martin McDonald from Doncaster Rovers (1997)	Free
445.	Danny Swailes from Bury (2005)	£15,000
446.	Efe Sodje from Stevenage Borough (1997)	£1,250
447.	David Morley from Doncaster Rovers (2004)	£30,000
448.	Neil Ross from Stockport County (2002)	Free
449.	Darren Tinson from Northwich Victoria (1996)	£25,000
450.	Graeme Tomlinson from Manchester United (1998)	£20,000

WHO ARE WE PLAYING? – 2

451. If The Silkmen were in opposition against The Bulls, what United would they be playing?

452. If The Silkmen were in opposition against The Cumbrians, what team would they be playing?

453. If The Silkmen were in opposition against The Shots, what 'Town' would they be playing?

454. If The Silkmen were in opposition against The Addicks, what team would they be playing?

455. If The Silkmen were in opposition against The Villains, what team would they be playing?

456. If The Silkmen were in opposition against The Clarets, what team would they be playing?

457. If The Silkmen were in opposition against The Sky Blues, what team would they be playing?

458. If The Silkmen were in opposition against The Monkey Hangers, what team would they be playing?

459. If The Silkmen were in opposition against The Baggies, what club would they be playing?

460. If The Silkmen were in opposition against The Red Devils, what club would they be playing?

DARREN TINSON

461. Darren was born in Connah's Quay, Wales, on 15 November in which year – 1965, 1967 or 1969?

462. At which Welsh club did Darren start his playing career in 1990?

463. In what position does Darren play?

464. Darren was captain of which club when they won the Conference play-off final 3-0 on penalties after drawing 1-1 against Aldershot in May 2005 at the Britannia Stadium, Stoke-on-Trent?

465. How many League appearances did Darren make during his seven years at Macclesfield Town – 243, 253 or 263?

466. Which non-League club did Darren join in 2008?

467. How many League goals did Darren score for The Silkmen – 5, 10 or 15?

468. When Darren signed for Macclesfield Town in February 1996, in what position was he originally brought to the club to play?

469. True or false: Darren is a qualified Chartered Physiotherapist?

470. For which non-League club did Darren make 74 (2) League appearances between August 2005 and May 2007?

471. *If The Silkmen visited Craven Cottage, what team would they be playing away?*

472. *If The Silkmen visited Portman Road, what team would they be playing away?*

473. *If The Silkmen visited Belle Vue, what 'Rovers' would they be playing away?*

474. *If The Silkmen visited Brunton Park, what 'United' would they be playing away?*

475. *If The Silkmen visited Valley Parade, what 'City' would they be playing away?*

476. *If The Silkmen visited Turf Moor, what team would they be playing away?*

477. *If The Silkmen visited Layer Road, what 'United' would they be playing away?*

478. *If The Silkmen visited Victoria Road, what double-barrelled team would they be playing away?*

479. *If The Silkmen visited Selhurst Park, what team would they be playing away?*

480. *If The Silkmen visited Whaddon Park, what Town would they be playing away?*

RICKIE LAMBERT

481. Rickie was born on 16 February 1982 in which north-west city?

482. At which club did Rickie make his professional debut as a substitute in 1998?

483. How many League appearances did Rickie make for The Silkmen – 26 (8), 36 (8) or 46 (8)?

484. Rickie joined Stockport County from Macclesfield Town in April 2002, for what transfer fee - £250,000, £275,000 or £300,000?

485. What was the transfer fee when Rickie joined Macclesfield Town from Blackpool in March 2001?

486. At which club did Rickie play the 2005/06 season, scoring 28 League goals in 64 League appearances?

487. While at Bristol Rovers Rickie achieved Goal of the Season in both 2006/07 and 2007/08, playing against which two clubs?

488. Which honour did Rickie win with Bristol Rovers in May 2007?

489. How many League goals did Rickie score during his time at Macclesfield Town – 4, 8 or 12?

490. On 16 February 2008, his 26th birthday, Rickie scored a goal for Bristol Rovers in a 5th round FA Cup tie, clinching a 1-0 win against which club?

GEORGE ABBEY

491.   How many seasons did George play at Macclesfield Town?

492.   How many League appearances did George make for Macclesfield Town during his playing career – 79 (21), 89 (21) or 99 (21)?

493.   Which Macclesfield Town manager signed George for the club?

494.   Against which team did George make his Macclesfield Town League debut during August 1999 in a 3-0 away defeat?

495.   What is George's middle name –Peterson, Parkinson or Pateson?

496.   In what position does George play?

497.   In which year was George born – 1977, 1978 or 1979?

498.   For which team did George sign when he left Macclesfield Town?

499.   How many League goals did George score for Macclesfield during his career?

500.   Against which team did George score the opening goal in a 3-2 League away win during April 2003?

POSITIONS THEY PLAYED – 1

Match up the player with his position

501.	Horace Williams	Centre forward
502.	Terry Lees	Midfielder
503.	Jonny Brain	Left back
504.	Graham Potter	Goalkeeper
505.	Rikki Baines	Right back
506.	Albert Valentine	Fullback
507.	Richard Edghill	Striker
508.	David Flitcroft	Defender/Midfielder
509.	Richard Tracey	Inside forward
510.	Dick Ray	Defender

511.   If The Silkmen were in opposition against The Gunners, what team would they be playing?

512.   If The Silkmen were in opposition against The Seagulls, what team would they be playing?

513.   If The Silkmen were in opposition against The Black Cats, what team would they be playing?

514.   If The Silkmen were in opposition against The Imps, what 'City' would they be playing?

515.   If The Silkmen were in opposition against The Reds, what former English two times European Cup winners would they be playing?

516.   If The Silkmen were in opposition against The Rams, what team would they be playing?

517.   If The Silkmen were in opposition against The Yellow Army, what team would they be playing?

518.   If The Silkmen were in opposition against The Cottagers, what team would they be playing?

519.   If The Silkmen were in opposition against The Citizens, what 'City' would they be playing?

520.   If The Silkmen were in opposition against The U's, can you name any one of the two 'Uniteds' they could be playing?

TOP FOOTBALL LEAGUE GOALSCORERS

Match up the player with the number of League goals he scored for Macclesfield Town

521.	Richie Barker	14
522.	Matthew Tipton	23
523.	John Parkin	19
524.	Kevin McIntyre	31
525.	John Miles	30
526.	John Askey	23
527.	Lee Glover	21
528.	Danny Whitaker	45
529.	Kyle Lightbourne	18
530.	Steve Wood	16

AWAY DAYS – 4

531. If The Silkmen visited Stamford Bridge, what team would they be playing away?

532. If The Silkmen visited Pride Park Stadium, what team would they be playing away?

533. If The Silkmen visited Saltergate, what team would they be playing away?

534. If The Silkmen visited Deva Stadium, what 'City' would they be playing away?

535. If The Silkmen visited Broadfield Stadium, what 'Town' would they be playing away?

536. If The Silkmen visited Fraser Eagle Stadium, what team would they be playing away?

537. If The Silkmen visited The Lawn, what team would they be playing away?

538. If The Silkmen visited The Valley, what team would they be playing away?

539. If The Silkmen visited Ashton Gate, what team would they be playing away?

540. If The Silkmen visited Park Lane, what team would they be playing away?

TOMMY WIDDRINGTON

541. Tommy was born on 1 October 1971 in which north-east city/town – Hartlepool, Darlington or Newcastle upon Tyne?

542. Which club did Tommy join in July 1996 for £300,000?

543. On 8 September 2007, which manager was fined £1,500 and served with a 10-match touchline ban for headbutting Tommy in a Conference League match between Salisbury City and Rushden & Diamonds?

544. At which First Division club did Tommy start his professional career in May 1990?

545. How many League appearances did Tommy make for The Silkmen – 38, 48 or 58?

546. In February 2005, for which club did Tommy sign?

547. During his two years at Macclesfield Town, how many League goals did Tommy score?

548. What squad number does Tommy wear at the club in question 546 – 8, 11 or 13?

549. Tommy has played at all 92 League grounds, but which ground in 2005 became his 92nd?

550. In what position does Tommy play?

AWAY DAYS – 5

551. If The Silkmen visited JJB Stadium, what team would they be playing away?

552. If The Silkmen visited Gresty Road, what team would they be playing away?

553. If The Silkmen visited Griffin Park, what team would they be playing away?

554. If The Silkmen visited Blundell Park, what 'Town' would they be playing away?

555. If The Silkmen visited St James's Park, what 'City' would they be playing away?

556. If The Silkmen visited the Reebok Stadium, what team would they be playing away?

557. If The Silkmen visited Elland Road, what team would they be playing away?

558. If The Silkmen visited Priestfield Stadium, what team would they be playing away?

559. If The Silkmen visited Brisbane Road, what team would they be playing away?

560. If The Silkmen were in opposition against The Hammers, what club would they be playing?

CHRIS PRIEST

561.   Chris was born in Leigh on 18 October in which year –
       1971, 1973 or 1975?

562.   At which Premiership club did Chris start his career as
       a trainee in June 1992?

563.   Chris scored a brace in a 3-1 home win for Macclesfield
       Town on 3 February 2001, against which opponents?

564.   From which club did Chris join Macclesfield Town on a
       free transfer in July 1999?

565.   How many League goals did Chris score for The
       Silkmen – 13, 17 or 21?

566.   Chris made his Macclesfield debut on 7 August 1999 in
       a 1-0 home win against which club?

567.   What happened to Chris for the first and only time as
       a Macclesfield player in the 4-0 defeat at Huddersfield
       Town on 13 March 2004?

568.   How many League appearances did Chris make during
       his five years for The Silkmen – 140 (10), 150 (10) or
       160 (10)?

569.   With which former Macclesfield Town manager did
       Chris link up again at Colwyn Bay in 2006?

570.   Against which club did Chris score his first goal for The
       Silkmen, in a 1-1 draw at home on 10 August 1999?

WHO ARE WE PLAYING? – 4

571.   If The Silkmen were in opposition against The
        Railwaymen, what team would they be playing?

572.   If The Silkmen were in opposition against The Robins,
        what 'City' would they be playing?

573.   If The Silkmen were in opposition against The
        Mariners, what team would they be playing?

574.   If The Silkmen were in opposition against The Vikings,
        what 'Rovers' would they be playing?

575.   If The Silkmen were in opposition against The Terriers,
        what 'Town' would they be playing?

576.   If The Silkmen were in opposition against The Eagles,
        what team would they be playing?

577.   If The Silkmen were in opposition against The Tractor
        Boys, what team would they be playing?

578.   If The Silkmen were in opposition against The
        Bantams, what team would they be playing?

579.   If The Silkmen were in opposition against The Exiles,
        what team would they be playing?

580.   If The Silkmen were in opposition against The Yellows,
        what team would they be playing?

KEVIN KEEN

581. Kevin was born on 25 February 1967 in which Buckinghamshire town – Amersham, Chesham or Burnham?

582. In what position did Kevin play?

583. Kevin had a one-month spell as caretaker manager at Moss Rose in 2001, replacing which manager who went on to be Director of Football?

584. How many England Youth caps did Kevin win – 9, 12 or 15?

585. Kevin joined The Silkmen in 2000, making his debut in September in a 3-1 home defeat in the 3rd round of the Worthington Cup, against which Premiership club?

586. How many League appearances did Kevin make for Macclesfield Town – 42, 52 or 62?

587. What transfer fee did Wolverhampton Wanderers pay in July 1993 for Kevin's services - £400,000, £500,000 or £600,000?

588. Which club paid Wolverhampton Wanderers £300,000 for Kevin in October 1994?

589. How many League goals did Kevin score for Macclesfield Town?

590. In September 2008, to which former Italian international and Chelsea player did Kevin hand over the manager's role at West Ham United?

FORMER AWAY GROUNDS

591. If The Silkmen had paid a visit to Maine Road in the past, what team would have been the home side?

592. If The Silkmen had paid a visit to Filbert Street in the past, what team would have been the home side?

593. If The Silkmen had paid a visit to Arsenal Stadium in the past, what team would have been the home side?

594. If The Silkmen had paid a visit to Ayresome Park in the past, what team would have been the home side?

595. If The Silkmen had paid a visit to Plough Lane in the past, what team would have been the home side?

596. If The Silkmen had paid a visit to The Goldstone Ground in the past, what team would have been the home side?

597. If The Silkmen had paid a visit to Highfield Road in the past, what team would have been the home side?

598. If The Silkmen had paid a visit to The Dell in the past, what team would have been the home side?

599. If The Silkmen had paid a visit to Elm Park in the past, what team would have been the home side?

600. If The Silkmen had paid a visit to The Baseball Ground in the past, what team would have been the home side?

SAMMY McIlROY

601. Sammy was born in Belfast on 2 August in which year – 1950, 1952 or 1954?

602. In May 2006 Sammy became the manager of which club?

603. At which club did Sammy start his professional career in 1971, going on to make 342 League appearances for them and scoring 57 League goals?

604. Sammy took Macclesfield Town into which Division of the Football League in 1997 for the first time in their history?

605. During his 15-year international playing career, how many appearances did Sammy make for Northern Ireland – 78, 88 or 98?

606. Sammy began his managerial career as a player/coach at Preston North End in 1991, acting as assistant to which former Manchester United player?

607. Sammy managed the Northern Ireland international team from 2000-03 and he was in charge for 28 games, but how many did he win?

608. In 2005 Sammy stood in for which manager at Morecambe after he suffered a heart attack?

609. Sammy played all his senior football in England apart from one spell in which other country in 1986?

610. In 1969 Sammy was the last Youth player at Manchester United to be signed by which legendary manager?

POT LUCK - 1

611. In season 2006/07 Macclesfield were beaten 6-1 by which reigning Premier League champions?

612. Which Premier League 'City' beat The Silkmen 7-0 in the 1998/99 FA Cup?

613. Which north-east club, the 2004 League Cup winners, beat Macclesfield in the competition three years earlier in season 2001/02?

614. In season 1998/99 Macclesfield finished as runners-up to which club in Division Three?

615. Macclesfield's George Abbey was chosen by his country to be part of their squad in which Cup competition in early 2004?

616. Who was Macclesfield's leading goalscorer in season 1999-2000 with 17 goals in all competitions?

617. Between 1874 and 1940 the club was known as Macclesfield Football & Athletic Club, Macclesfield FC and what other name with the word 'field' in it?

618. The club's first ever home jersey comprised stripes of which two colours?

619. What is the lion rampant holding in the club's crest?

620. In season 1998/99 Macclesfield Town finished bottom of Nationwide League Division Two, but which Premier League side in season 2008/09 won the Division?

IAN BRIGHTWELL

621. Ian was born on 9 April 1968 in which English county?

622. Ian made his Macclesfield debut on 30 August 2004 in a 2-1 away defeat at which south-east club?

623. Who was Ian's assistant manager at Macclesfield Town in 2007/08?

624. In October 2008, which former club did Ian return to as a temporary coach?

625. How many League appearances did Ian make for The Silkmen – 17, 21 or 25?

626. At which club did Ian start his professional career in 1986?

627. How many England Under-21 appearances did Ian make for his country, scoring two goals – 4, 8 or 12?

628. What injury, sustained in 1993, kept Ian from playing for over a year?

629. In what position did Ian play during his playing days?

630. True or false: Ian is the son of Olympic gold medallist Ann Packer?

THE BOB LORD
CHALLENGE TROPHY

631.   Bob Lord was the former chairman of which Lancashire
       club when he presented the Bob Lord Challenge
       Trophy to the Conference in 1979?

632.   Can you name either of the two names by which the
       competition was known in season 2008/09?

633.   The Silkmen won the trophy in 1994, beating which
       'Town' in the final?

634.   Following on from the previous question, what was the
       aggregate score in the final – 4-1, 5-2 or 6-3?

635.   In what season during the late 1980s did Macclesfield
       first compete in the competition?

636.   In season 1992/93 The Silkmen reached the semi-finals
       and the competition had which sponsor? (Clue: alcohol
       awareness)

637.   Can you name the 'Rovers' that defeated Macclesfield
       in the 1995/96 final?

638.   Following on from the previous question, can you
       name the British sports manufacturer that sponsored
       the competition? (Clue: squash ball manufacturers)

639.   Can you name the club that beat The Silkmen in the
       1996/97 final but finished as runners-up to
       Macclesfield in the Football Conference?

640.   In season 1992/93 Macclesfield were semi-finalists in
       the competition but were beaten by which team
       known as 'The Vics'?

DANNY WHITAKER

641. Danny was born on 14 November 1980 in which Cheshire Town?

642. In what position does Danny play?

643. In season 2002/03 Danny made 41 League appearances for Macclesfield Town, scoring how many League goals?

644. Which club did Danny join in June 2008 on a free transfer?

645. How many League appearances did Danny make for The Silkmen – 156 (15), 166 (15) or 176 (15)?

646. Danny played his last game for Macclesfield Town on 6 May 2006 in a 3-2 away win at which West Country club?

647. What nickname was Danny given at Oldham Athletic?

648. How many League goals did Danny score for Macclesfield Town – 19, 21 or 23?

649. Which club did Danny join after leaving Macclesfield Town in June 2006?

650. In which season did Danny win Player of the Year at Macclesfield Town – 2003/04, 2004/05 or 2005/06?

KYLE LIGHTBOURNE

651. In which year was Kyle born – 1966, 1967 or 1968?

652. For which team did Kyle play between 1993 and 1997?

653. How many League appearances did Kyle make during his Macclesfield Town career – 53, 63 or 73?

654. Against which team did Kyle make his Macclesfield Town League debut during August 2001?

655. What is Kyle's middle name – Lawrence, Leeroy or Lavince?

656. For which country did Kyle win 40 international caps, scoring 16 goals?

657. Against which team did Kyle score Macclesfield's first goal in a 2-1 home League win during January 2002?

658. Which Macclesfield manager signed Kyle for the club?

659. How many League goals did Kyle score in his Macclesfield Town career – 14, 21 or 28?

660. For which team did Kyle play between 1998 and 2001?

GRAEME TOMLINSON

661. Where in Hertfordshire was Graeme born on 10 December 1975 – Hertford, Watford or Bishop's Stortford?

662. In what position did Graeme play?

663. What is Graeme's middle name - Murdoch, Michael or Martin?

664. Graeme made his Macclesfield debut on 11 August 1998 in a 3-1 home win in the League Cup, against which opponents?

665. How many League appearances did Graeme make for The Silkmen – 22 (24), 32 (24) or 42 (24)?

666. At which club did Graeme start his professional career in August 1993?

667. How many League goals did Graeme score for Macclesfield Town – 3, 6 or 9?

668. Graeme scored a hat-trick in an FA Cup game in a 4-1 home win on 5 December 1998, against which club?

669. Which Macclesfield manager signed Graeme from Manchester United in July 1998?

670. For which club did Graeme make 56 League appearances, scoring 6 League goals, the highest number of appearances he made in the Football League for any club?

THE ASSOCIATE MEMBERS' CUP/
THE FOOTBALL LEAGUE TROPHY

671. Can you name the sponsors of the competition in season 2008/09?

672. In what season during the mid-1980s did the competition receive a sponsor for the first time?

673. Name the 'Rovers' that put Macclesfield out of the 2002/03 competition on the away goals rule.

674. Can you name the Welsh club that put The Silkmen out of the 1998/99 competition?

675. In season 2000/01 The Silkmen were knocked out of the League Cup by which side?

676. Can you name the 'Danny' who scored Macclesfield's only goal in the 2003/04 competition?

677. In season 2008/09 The Silkmen beat which team 1-0 away in League Two, the side that won the inaugural Associate Members' Cup in season 1983/84?

678. Which former English domestic Double winners knocked The Silkmen out of the competition in season 1997/98?

679. Which team beginning with the letter 'D' knocked The Silkmen out of the 2001/02 competition?

680. Name the Greater Manchester side that put The Silkmen out of the 1999/2000 competition on the Golden Goal rule.

KEVIN McINTYRE

681.   Kevin was born in Liverpool on 23 December in which year – 1977, 1978 or 1979?

682.   At which club did Kevin start his professional career in August 1996?

683.   Kevin made his League debut for Macclesfield Town on Boxing Day 2004 in a goalless draw away against which club?

684.   Which honour did Kevin win with Chester City in May 2004?

685.   How many League goals did Kevin score for The Silkmen – 8, 12 or 16?

686.   Which club did Kevin join for £50,000 in January 2008?

687.   Against which former club did Kevin score on both New Year's Eve 2005 and Boxing Day 2006, with Macclesfield winning 1-0 and 3-0 respectively?

688.   How many League appearances did Kevin make for The Silkmen – 124, 134 or 144?

689.   Kevin was handed a red card only once during his four years at Macclesfield, in a 3-1 away defeat on 19 August 2006 at which club?

690.   In what position does Kevin play?

DEREK KEVAN

691. In what year did Derek arrive at Moss Rose?

692. What was Derek's nickname during his playing career –
The Bus, The Ox or The Tank?

693. Name the Midlands club that Kevin was playing for when
he was the joint-leading goalscorer in the English First
Division in season 1961/62.

694. Derek was capped by England 14 times, scoring how
many goals for his country – 6, 8 or 10?

695. At what 'Avenue' did Derek begin his playing career in
1952?

696. Can you name the year or the hosts when Derek scored
twice for England at the World Cup finals?

697. When Derek left the club in question 693, what London
club did he join?

698. From 1963-65 Derek scored a remarkable 48 League
goals in 67 games for which Lancashire side?

699. Name the 'United' that Derek joined in 1966.

700. Derek scored four goals for which 'Town' in season
1966/67?

BEN SEDGEMORE

701. Where in the Midlands was Ben born on 5 August 1975 – Wolverhampton, Birmingham or Dudley?

702. How many League appearances did Ben make for The Silkmen – 84 (18), 94 (18) or 104 (18)?

703. Ben joined Macclesfield Town from Mansfield Town in March 1998, for what transfer fee - £15,000, £20,000 or £25,000?

704. In January 2006 Ben joined which non-League club nicknamed The Hawks, where he played 23 League games?

705. How many League goals did Ben score for Macclesfield Town – 3, 6 or 9?

706. True or false: as at 2008, Ben is on the Football Referees Committee?

707. At which club did Ben spend three years (1993-96) at Youth level?

708. Which club did Ben join in February 2001 from Macclesfield Town, going on to make 108 League appearances for them?

709. Ben made his League debut for Macclesfield on 21 March 1998 in a 2-1 home win against which club?

710. In what position does Ben play?

MICHAEL WELCH

711.   What nationality is Michael?

712.   From which team did Michael sign to join Macclesfield in 2001?

713.   In what position does Michael play?

714.   In which year was Michael born in Crewe – 1981, 1982 or 1983?

715.   Which team did Michael join when he left Macclesfield Town in 2005?

716.   How many League goals did Michael score during his Macclesfield Town career – 5, 6 or 7?

717.   Against which team did Michael score for Macclesfield in a 3-1 away League win during September 2002?

718.   Against which team did Michael score Macclesfield's first goal in a 2-1 home League win during January 2005?

719.   Which Macclesfield Town manager signed Michael for the club in 2001?

720.   True or false: Michael made 114 League appearances for Macclesfield Town during his career?

POSITIONS THEY PLAYED – 2

Match up the player with his position

721.	Tony Waiters	Full back
722.	Brian Fidler	Inside Right
723.	Dennis Fidler	Wing Half
724.	Jamie Tolley	Goalkeeper
725.	Rae Ingram	Centre forward
726.	Ian Elsby	Midfielder
727.	Lennie Butt	Goalkeeper
728.	Wilf Hall	Right back
729.	Sean Hessey	Winger
730.	Dave Roberts	Defender

THE SWINGING 60s

731.   Can you name the 'Roger' whose Testimonial Match in May 1960 saw The Silkmen beat Accrington Stanley 7-1?

732.   Following on from the previous question, name the player from Stoke City who guested for Macclesfield for that match and who later arrived at Moss Rose as the club's new player/manager.

733.   Macclesfield won the Cheshire League in season 1961/62, but which team carried off English Football's coveted Double that season?

734.   Which Cup competition did The Silkmen win three times during this decade?

735.   Following on from the previous question, name any of the teams that Macclesfield beat in the finals.

736.   Which London-based Premier League team in season 2008/09 knocked The Silkmen out of the FA Cup in season 1967/68?

737.   Name the Premier League team in season 2008/09 that knocked The Silkmen out of the Inter-League Challenge Cup in season 1962/63.

738.   Can you name the Cup competition that The Silkmen won in season 1966/67 after defeating Runcorn 3-0 on aggregate in the final?

739.   Following on from question 733, name any other year during this decade in which Macclesfield Town won the Cheshire League.

740.   In what season did Macclesfield appear on the Football Pools coupon for the first time in the club's history thanks to qualifying for the 3rd round of the FA Cup?

PLAYING YEARS AT THE CLUB – 2

*Match up the player with the period he spent
at Macclesfield Town*

741.	John Askey	2002-07
742.	Ryan Price	1966-67
743.	Bill Myerscough	1997-99
744.	Kieron Durkan	1984-2003
745.	Paul Harsley	1963-72
746.	Wilf Hall	1995-99
747.	John Miles	1998-2001
748.	Martin Clark	2004-06
749.	Efe Sodje	2005-07
750.	David Morley	1995-96

751. How many times during the decade did The Silkmen win the Cheshire Senior Cup?

752. Following on from the previous question, can you name any year in which they won it?

753. In August 1970 the first ever Macclesfield match to be decided by penalties was in which pre-season Cup competition?

754. Following on from the previous question, can you name the team that The Silkmen beat?

755. What was the name of the trophy won at Wembley by Macclesfield on 2 May 1970 for the first and only time in the club's history in what was the inaugural edition of the competition?

756. Following on from the previous question, can you name the 'United' that Macclesfield beat 2-0 in the final?

757. In what year during the decade did The Silkmen win their second Northern Premier League championship title?

758. In the early 1970s Macclesfield Ladies' FC played their first ever game. What is their nickname?

759. What did a Goole Town defender break at the Star Lane end in October 1970, causing the game to be held up for several minutes?

760. Can you name the future England manager who scored twice for Scunthorpe United in their 4-2 win over Macclesfield in an FA Cup 1st round replay in season 1969/70?

MATCH THE YEAR – 3

Match up the event with the year it took place

761. **Richie Barker moved to Rotherham United for £100,000** 1951

762. **Wilf Hall joined Macclesfield Town** 1999

763. **Brian Fidler made his Silkmen debut** 1981

764. **The new Main Stand was built at Moss Rose** 1994

765. **Jack Smith became player/manager at Macclesfield Town** 2001

766. **John Askey's testimonial was played against a Manchester United XI** 1966

767. **Jimmy Williams became manager of The Silkmen** 1971

768. **An attendance of 31,086 watched the Division Two game at Maine Road between Manchester City and Macclesfield Town** 1963

769. **The first ever sponsors of Macclesfield Town, Sachs Dolmar UK, appeared on the shirts** 1968

770. **Macclesfield Town Ladies – The Silkgirls - played the first match of their very first season** 1980

THE NEW ROMANCE 80s

771. Can you name the Manchester United manager who officially opened the club's new all-weather pitch on 24 March 1981?

772. How many times during the decade did The Silkmen lift the Cheshire Senior Cup?

773. Following on from the previous question, name any year during the 1980s when The Silkmen finished as runners-up in the Cheshire Senior Cup.

774. In what year during the 1980s did Macclesfield win the Northern Premier League?

775. Following on from the previous question, how many times did The Silkmen finish as runners-up in the Northern Premier League?

776. Can you name the non-League "City" beginning with the letter "W" which thumped The Silkmen 5-1 in the FA Cup in season 1982-83?

777. Name the former League club, which folded at the end of the 2005-06 season, which was the last team The Silkmen played in the decade, winning 4-0 at home on 30th December 1989.

778. In the summer of 1984 Macclesfield signed two players from Stafford Rangers. Name any one of the two players who proved to be key signings for the club.

779. Can you name the Macclesfield manager who quit the game in May 1985 after the final match of the season, stating in an interview with the Express Advertiser that "the game is not worth dying for"?

780. In which season during the 1980s did The Silkmen play in The Vauxhall Conference for the first time?

NON-LEAGUE MANAGERS

*Match up the manager with the period he
was in charge at Macclesfield Town*

781.	Peter Wragg	*1955-58*
782.	John Collins (player/manager)	*1978-80*
783.	Albert Leake (player/manager)	*1986-93*
784.	William Edwards (player/manager)	*1968-72*
785.	Brian Booth	*1947-49*
786.	Dave Connor	*1936-37*
787.	Frank Beaumont (player/manager)	*1981-85*
788.	James Stevenson	*1975-76*
789.	Bert Swindells	*1976-78*
790.	Phil Staley	*1963-67*

POT LUCK

791. Can you name the 'United' that were Macclesfield's first ever opponents in the Vauxhall Conference in season 1987/88?

792. Following on from the previous question, name the striker who scored The Silkmen's first ever goal in the Vauxhall Conference.

793. What Senior Cup did Macclesfield win in 1994 for the first and only time in the club's history?

794. How many times have The Silkmen finished as runners-up in the Cheshire Senior Cup – 7, 9 or 11?

795. Name the member of the band 'New Order' who is a massive fan of The Silkmen.

796. Name the teenager striker who scored his first senior goal for The Silkmen in their 2-1 win over Barnet on 25 April 2009.

797. Following on from the previous question, can you name the club's traditional rivals from their time together in the Cheshire League and later the Northern Premier League and Conference?

798. A new club badge was to be introduced at the start of which season only for it to be delayed until later in the season as the majority of Silkmen fans did not like it?

799. During the 1996 European Championships held in England, which eventual winners of the tournament used Moss Rose as their training camp?

800. Can you name the former professional wrestler turned actor who picked Macclesfield Town out of a hat when the Soccer AM crew asked him to choose a football team to support?

ANSWERS

CLUB HISTORY & RECORDS

1. 1874
2. Moss Rose
3. Albert Valentine
4. 1997/98
5. 1946
6. John Askey
7. Chris Priest
8. Northwich Victoria
9. The Silkmen
10. Torquay United

ALAN NAVARRO

11. Liverpool
12. Crewe Alexandra
13. 2004
14. Tranmere Rovers
15. 70 (11 and 59)
16. 3
17. 2007
18. MK Dons
19. Accrington Stanley
20. Paul Ince

CLUB HONOURS

21.	FA Challenge Trophy winners (1st time)	1970
22.	Bob Lord Trophy winners	1994
23.	Combination runners-up for the 1st time	1891
24.	Cheshire Senior Cup winners (20th time)	2000
25.	GM Vauxhall Conference champions (2nd time)	1997
26.	Northern Premier League champions (1st time)	1969
27.	Cheshire County League champions (1st time)	1932
28.	Third Division runners-up	1998
29.	Northern Premier League Challenge Cup winners	1987
30.	League Two play-off semi-finalists	2005

THE LEAGUE CUP

31. Hartlepool United

32.	Preston North End
33.	Cardiff City
34.	Hull City
35.	Birmingham City
36.	Middlesbrough
37.	Sheffield United
38.	Leicester City
39.	Leeds United
40.	Bradford City

WHERE DID THEY GO? – 1

41.	Carl Regan	MK Dons
42.	Paul Harsley	Port Vale
43.	John Miles	Accrington Stanley
44.	Alan Fettis	Bury
45.	Neil Howarth	Cheltenham Town
46.	Robbie Doyle	Dundalk
47.	John Coleman	Rhyl Town
48.	Lee Martin	Huddersfield Town
49.	Luke Dimech	Valletta
50.	Martin Clark	Albion Rovers

DANNY SWAILES

51.	1979
52.	Bury
53.	Kidderminster Harriers
54.	Carlisle United
55.	2
56.	Defender
57.	2007
58.	MK Dons
59.	5
60.	Swindon Town

FOOTBALL LEAGUE MANAGERS

61.	Sammy McIlroy	1993-2000
62.	Peter Davenport	2000
63.	Brian Horton	2004-06

64.	Paul Ince	2006-07
65.	Kevin Keen	2001
66.	John Askey	2003-04
67.	Ian Brightwell	2007-08
68.	Gil Prescott	2001
69.	David Moss	2001-03
70.	Keith Alexander	2008-09

2008/2009

71. West Ham United
72. Shrewsbury Town
73. Luton Town
74. Harlow Town
75. Shaun Brisley (in a 2-0 League Cup win against Blackpool)
76. Morecambe
77. Johnstone's Paint Trophy (Northern Section 1st round)
78. Blackpool
79. Simon Yeo (v. Luton Town)
80. Everton

NATIONALITIES – 1

81.	Kyle Lightbourne	Bermudian
82.	Tony Williams	Welsh
83.	Patrece Liburd	Kittitian & Nevisian
84.	James McNulty	English
85.	David Morley	English
86.	Fola Onibuje	Nigerian
87.	Luke Dimech	Maltese
88.	Robbie Doyle	Irish
89.	Karl Munroe	English
90.	Clyde Wijnhard	Dutch Colony Surinam

2007/2008

91. Stockport County
92. Bradford City
93. Francis Green
94. Bury
95. Hereford United

96. Gareth Evans

97. Rotherham United

98. Chesterfield

99. Wrexham

100. Hereford United

WHERE DID THEY COME FROM? – 1

101.	Neil Harvey	Retford United
102.	Richard Irving	Nottingham Forest
103.	Kevin McIntyre	Chester City
104.	David Flitcroft	Rochdale
105.	Michael Husbands	Port Vale
106.	Neil Moore	Burnley
107.	Richard Edghill	Bradford City
108.	Paul Ince	Swindon Town
109.	Terry Dudfield	Worcester City
110.	Harry Lovatt	Northampton Town

PAUL INCE - 1

111. Inter Milan

112. Liverpool

113. 2006

114. The Guv'nor

115. Wolverhampton Wanderers

116. Manchester United

117. An FA Cup winners' medal (with Man United in 1990)

118. Swindon Town

119. Blackburn Rovers

120. 2 (1992/93 and 1993/94)

LEAGUE POSITIONS

121.	2007/08, 50 points	19th
122.	1997/98, 82 points	2nd
123.	2002/03, 54 points	16th
124.	1999/2000, 65 points	13th
125.	2006/07, 48 points	22nd
126.	2003/04, 52 points	20th
127.	1998/99, 43 points	24th

128.	*2004/05, 75 points*	*5th*
129.	*2000/01, 56 points*	*14th*
130.	*2005/06, 54 points*	*17th*

DAVID FLITCROFT

131. **Gary Flitcroft**
132. **Preston North End**
133. **Lincoln City**
134. **Chester City**
135. **Rochdale**
136. **Bury**
137. **Bolton (Bolton Wanderers)**
138. **Hyde United**
139. **Rochdale**
140. **Chester City**

KEITH ALEXANDER

141. **Nottingham**
142. **Notts County**
143. **The FA Vase**
144. **£7,000**
145. **Grimsby Town**
146. **Centre forward**
147. **Ian Brightwell**
148. **Peterborough United**
149. **Lincoln City**
150. **St Lucia**

DEREK PARLANE

151. **Glasgow Rangers**
152. **1988**
153. **Leeds United**
154. **Manchester City**
155. **Billy McNeill**
156. **Crystal Palace**
157. **Belgium**
158. **Swansea City**
159. **Reebok**

160. *Airdrieonians*

SQUAD NUMBERS 2008/09 – 1

161.	Simon Yeo	10
162.	Chris Hirst	21
163.	Jonny Brain	1
164.	John Rooney	14
165.	Richard Walker	5
166.	Lee Bell	7
167.	Terry Dunfield	25
168.	James Jennings	19
169.	Ahmed Deen	3
170.	Martin Gritton	9

2006/2007

171. 20
172. Darlington
173. Stockport County
174. Kevin McIntyre
175. Lincoln City
176. Accrington Stanley
177. Dave Morley
178. Matty McNeil
179. John Miles
180. Chester City

WHERE DID THEY GO? – 2

181.	Tommy Lee	Chesterfield
182.	Martin Carruthers	Boston United
183.	Tony Bullock	Lincoln City
184.	Tony Barras	Witton Albion
185.	Colin Little	Halifax Town
186.	Michael Carr	Northwich Victoria
187.	Chris Bettney	Worksop Town
188.	Matty McNeil	Stockport County
189.	Martin Bullock	Wycombe Wanderers
190.	Michael Briscoe	Hucknall Town

NEIL HOWARTH

191. Sammy McIlroy
192. Farnworth
193. 2
194. 1994/95
195. 1999
196. Cheltenham Town
197. £7,000
198. 1997/98
199. Telford United
200. Kidderminster Harriers

WHERE DID THEY COME FROM? – 2

201.	Peter Jackson	Hyde United
202.	Jamie Milligan	Blackpool
203.	Steve Davis	Oxford United
204.	Simon Collins	Plymouth Argyle
205.	Derek Kevan	Stockport County
206.	Paul Morgan	Bury
207.	Jonny Brain	Port Vale
208.	Neil MacKenzie	Mansfield Town
209.	Simon Davies	Luton Town
210.	Karl Munroe	Swansea City

SIMON YEO

211. Hyde United
212. John
213. 2008
214. Keith Alexander
215. Lincoln City
216. Striker
217. 1973
218. Port Vale
219. Notts County
220. Luton Town

SQUAD NUMBERS 2008/09 – 2

221.	Danny Thomas	12

222.	Izak Reid	2
223.	Matthew Towns	13
224.	Francis Green	8
225.	Sean Hessey	4
226.	Neil Harvey	15
227.	Jamie Tolley	11
228.	Gareth Evans	26
229.	Shaun Brisley	16
230.	Nick Blackman	20

JOHN ASKEY

231.	Striker and right winger
232.	1987
233.	31
234.	Darlington
235.	Rochdale
236.	1964
237.	3
238.	Doncaster Rovers
239.	4
240.	181: 136 (45)

NATIONALITIES – 2

241.	Matthew Tipton	Welsh
242.	Joaquin Medinilla-Cabotti	Spanish
243.	Martin Gritton	Scottish
244.	Ahmed Deen	Sierra Leonean
245.	Dean Delaney	Irish
246.	Asmir Begovic	Herzegovian
247.	Boaz Myhill	American
248.	Terry Dunfield	Canadian
249.	Alan Navarro	English
250.	Neil Harvey	Barbadian

1990s

251.	Altrincham
252.	Merthyr Tydfil
253.	Cheltenham, Farnborough, Kettering, Slough and Yeovil

254.   Chesterfield

255.   Bath City

256.   Bromsgrove Rovers

257.   Bath City (away), Slough Town (home) and Hednesford Town (home)

258.   Hull City

259.   Manchester City

260.   Carlisle United

FA CUP WINS

261.	1972/73, 2nd qualifying round	Macclesfield Town 3-0 Glossop
262.	1997/98, 1st round	Hartlepool United 2-4 Macclesfield Town
263.	2006/07, 2nd round	Macclesfield Town 2-1 Hartlepool United
264.	1987/88, 2nd round	Macclesfield Town 4-0 Rotherham United
265.	1982/83, 4th qualifying round	Macclesfield Town 3-1 Stafford Rangers
266.	1967/68, 2nd round	Macclesfield Town 2-0 Spennymoor United
267.	1998/99, 2nd round	Macclesfield Town 4-1 Cambridge United
268.	2001/02, 2nd round	Macclesfield Town 4-1 Swansea City
269.	1987/88, 1st round	Macclesfield Town 4-2 Carlisle United
270.	1975/76, 4th qualifying round	Mexborough Town 1-2 Macclesfield Town

2005/2006

271.   Leyton Orient

272.   Nottingham Forest

273.   Paul Harsley

274.   Cambridge, Hereford and Rotherham

275.   Stockport County

276.   Bristol Rovers

277. **Marcus Richardson**

278. **Wycombe Wanderers**

279. **Cardiff City**

280. **Carlisle United**

TOP FOOTBALL LEAGUE APPEARANCES

281.	**Danny Whitaker**	*171*
282.	**Steve Hitchen**	*151*
283.	**Darren Tinson**	*263*
284.	**Kevin McIntyre**	*134*
285.	**Michael Welsh**	*114*
286.	**Matthew Tipton**	*164*
287.	**John Askey**	*181*
288.	**Chris Priest**	*150*
289.	**Danny Adams**	*148*
290.	**Steve Wilson**	*134*

2004/2005

291. **Matthew Tipton**

292. **Hartlepool United**

293. **Mansfield Town**

294. **Alfreton Town**

295. **Rushden & Diamonds**

296. **Notts County (on 25 January 2005)**

297. **Lincoln City**

298. **Paul Harsley**

299. **Hull City**

300. **Tranmere Rovers**

EFE SODJE

301. **1972**

302. **Central defender**

303. **Macclesfield Town**

304. **Nigeria**

305. **83**

306. **40**

307. **A bandana**

308. **6**

309. *Luton Town*

310. *Bury*

DANNY THOMAS

311. **Left winger (midfield)**

312. **1981**

313. **Hereford United**

314. **Aldershot**

315. **False**

316. **Bradford City**

317. **Ian Brightwell**

318. **Boston United**

319. **Nottingham Forest**

320. **Justin**

BRIAN HORTON

321. **Hednesford**

322. **Port Vale**

323. **£30,000**

324. **Luton Town**

325. **Port Vale**

326. **47**

327. **Manager of the Month award**

328. **Port Vale, Brighton & Hove Albion and Hull City (he did not manage Luton Town)**

329. **John Askey**

330. **684: 610 (74)**

SEAN HESSEY

331. **Central defender**

332. **Huddersfield Town**

333. **Peter**

334. **Chester City**

335. **Kilmarnock**

336. **Ian Brightwell**

337. **Keith Alexander**

338. **False: he never scored a goal**

339. **English**

340.   1978

PLAYING YEARS AT THE CLUB – 1

341.	George Abbey	1999-2004
342.	Mike Lake	1986-89
343.	Albert Valentine	1933-34
344.	Rae Ingram	1998-2001
345.	Martin Bullock	2005-07
346.	Tony Waiters	1958-59
347.	David Flitcroft	2003-04
348.	Neil Mitchell	1996-98
349.	Joe Rogers	1893-94
350.	John Butcher	1989

AWAY DAYS – 1

351.   Manchester City
352.   Leicester City
353.   Hartlepool United
354.   Lincoln City
355.   Gravesend & Northfleet
356.   Sunderland
357.   Luton Town
358.   Huddersfield Town
359.   West Bromwich Albion
360.   Halifax Town

MATCH THE YEAR – 1

361.   2008
362.   1968
363.   1960
364.   1946
365.   1970
366.   1996
367.   1994
368.   1911
369.   1884
370.   1932

JAMIE TOLLEY

371. Shrewsbury Town

372. 16 years and 193 days

373. Wales

374. Midfielder

375. Luton Town

376. Brian Horton

377. MK Dons

378. Accrington Stanley

379. Chester City

380. 1983

CAPS FOR MY COUNTRY

381. Kyle Lightbourne   40 Bermuda caps

382. Andrejus Tereskinas   56 Lithuania caps

383. Paul Ince   53 England caps

384. Luke Dimech   60 Malta caps

385. Keith Alexander   3 St Lucia caps

386. Neil Harvey   3 Barbados caps

387. Derek Kevan   14 England caps

388. Martin Nash   38 Canada caps

389. Simon Davies   1 Wales cap

390. Derek Parlane   12 Scotland caps

WHO ARE WE PLAYING? – 1

391. Blackpool

392. Mansfield Town

393. Dagenham & Redbridge

394. Barnsley

395. Barnet and Brentford

396. Plymouth Argyle

397. Cardiff City

398. Accrington Stanley

399. Bristol Rovers

400. Burton Albion

MATCH THE YEAR – 2

401. 1962

402.	1891
403.	1993
404.	1979
405.	2000
406.	1955
407.	1999
408.	2007
409.	2003
410.	1998

AWAY DAYS – 2

411.	Birmingham City
412.	Cardiff City
413.	Northampton Town
414.	Bristol Rovers
415.	Altrincham
416.	Blackburn Rovers
417.	Coventry City
418.	Cambridge United
419.	Bury
420.	Burton Albion

JON PARKIN

421.	Barnsley
422.	'The Beast'
423.	63 (2)
424.	York City
425.	22
426.	£270,000
427.	30
428.	Barnsley
429.	Preston North End
430.	Central defender

PAUL INCE - 2

431.	Ian Brightwell
432.	True
433.	MK Dons

434. Midfielder
435. True
436. West Ham United
437. 2
438. False: Macclesfield lost 3-2
439. Walsall
440. Ian Brightwell

TRANSFERS

441.	Kevin Keen from Stoke City (2000)	Free
442.	Ben Sedgemore from Mansfield Town (1998)	£25,000
443.	Pat Connolly from Crewe Alexandra (1962)	£1,250
444.	Martin McDonald from Doncaster Rovers (1997)	£20,000
445.	Danny Swailes from Bury (2005)	£40,000
446.	Efe Sodje from Stevenage Borough (1997)	£30,000
447.	David Morley from Doncaster Rovers (2004)	£15,000
448.	Neil Ross from Stockport County (2002)	£30,000
449.	Darren Tinson from Northwich Victoria (1996)	£10,000
450.	Graeme Tomlinson from Manchester United (1998)	Free

WHO ARE WE PLAYING? – 2

451. Hereford United
452. Carlisle United
453. Aldershot Town
454. Charlton Athletic
455. Aston Villa
456. Burnley
457. Coventry City
458. Hartlepool United
459. West Bromwich Albion
460. Manchester United

DARREN TINSON

461. 1969
462. Colwyn Bay
463. Defender
464. Shrewsbury Town
465. 263

466. *Nantwich Town*

467. *5*

468. *Right back*

469. *True*

470. *Burton Albion*

AWAY DAYS – 3

471. *Fulham*

472. *Ipswich Town*

473. *Doncaster Rovers*

474. *Carlisle United*

475. *Bradford City*

476. *Burnley*

477. *Colchester United (ground now known as the Colchester Community Stadium)*

478 *Dagenham & Redbridge*

479. *Crystal Palace*

480. *Cheltenham Town*

RICKIE LAMBERT

481. *Liverpool*

482. *Blackpool*

483. *36 (8)*

484. *£300,000*

485. *Free transfer*

486. *Rochdale*

487. *Swindon Town 2006/07 and Luton Town 2007/08*

488. *League Two play-off winners*

489. *8*

490. *Southampton*

GEORGE ABBEY

491. *5: 1999-2004*

492. *79 (21)*

493. *Sammy McIlroy*

494. *Darlington*

495. *Peterson*

496. *Defender*

497.	1978
498.	Port Vale
499.	1
500.	Shrewsbury Town

POSITIONS THEY PLAYED – 1

501.	Horace Williams	Inside forward
502.	Terry Lees	Defender/Midfielder
503.	Jonny Brain	Goalkeeper
504.	Graham Potter	Fullback
505.	Rikki Baines	Defender
506.	Albert Valentine	Centre forward
507.	Richard Edghill	Right back
508.	David Flitcroft	Midfielder
509.	Richard Tracey	Striker
510.	Dick Ray	Left back

WHO ARE WE PLAYING? – 3

511.	Arsenal
512.	Brighton & Hove Albion
513.	Sunderland
514.	Lincoln City
515.	Nottingham Forest
516.	Derby County
517.	Canvey Island
518.	Fulham
519.	Manchester City
520.	Colchester United and Oxford United

TOP FOOTBALL LEAGUE GOALSCORERS

521.	Richie Barker	23
522.	Matthew Tipton	45
523.	John Parkin	30
524.	Kevin McIntyre	16
525.	John Miles	21
526.	John Askey	31
527.	Lee Glover	18
528.	Danny Whitaker	23

| 529. | Kyle Lightbourne | 14 |
| 530. | Steve Wood | 19 |

AWAY DAYS – 4

531. Chelsea
532. Derby County
533. Chesterfield
534. Chester City
535. Crawley Town
536. Accrington Stanley
537. Forest Green Rovers
538. Charlton Athletic
539. Bristol City
540. Canvey Island

TOMMY WIDDRINGTON

541. Newcastle upon Tyne
542. Grimsby Town
543. Garry Hill
544. Southampton
545. 58
546. Salisbury City
547. None
548. 13
549. Edgeley Park, Stockport County
550. Midfielder

AWAY DAYS – 5

551. Wigan Athletic
552. Crewe Alexandra
553. Brentford
554. Grimsby Town
555. Exeter City
556. Bolton Wanderers
557. Leeds United
558. Gillingham
559. Leyton Orient
560. West Ham United

CHRIS PRIEST

561.   1973
562.   Everton
563.   Plymouth Argyle
564.   Chester City
565.   13
566.   Northampton Town
567.   He was sent off
568.   140 (10)
569.   Peter Davenport
570.   Stoke City

WHO ARE WE PLAYING? – 4

571.   Crewe Alexandra
572.   Bristol City
573.   Grimsby Town
574.   Doncaster Rovers
575.   Huddersfield Town
576.   Crystal Palace
577.   Ipswich Town
578.   Bradford City
579.   Chester City
580.   Cambridge United

KEVIN KEEN

581.   Amersham
582.   Midfielder
583.   Gil Prescott
584.   15
585.   Middlesbrough
586.   62
587.   £600,000
588.   Stoke City
589.   2
590.   Gianfranco Zola

FORMER AWAY GROUNDS

591.   Manchester City

592.   Leicester City

593.   Arsenal

594.   Middlesbrough

595.   Wimbledon

596.   Brighton & Hove Albion

597.   Coventry City

598.   Southampton

599.   Reading

600.   Derby County

SAMMY McILROY

601.   1954

602.   Morecambe

603.   Manchester United

604.   League Division Three

605.   88

606.   John McGrath

607.   4 wins, all in the first year

608.   Jim Harvey

609.   Sweden, playing for Orgryte IS

610.   Sir Matt Busby

POT LUCK - 1

611.   Chelsea

612.   Coventry City

613.   Middlesbrough

614.   Notts County

615.   The 2004 African Cup of Nations

616.   Richie Barker

617.   Hallifield

618.   Amber and black

619.   A wheat sheaf

620.   Fulham

IAN BRIGHTWELL

621.   Leicestershire (Lutterworth)

622.   Southend United

623.   Asa Hartford

624. Port Vale
625. 21
626. Manchester City
627. 4
628. He snapped his patella tendon
629. Defender
630. True

THE BOB LORD CHALLENGE TROPHY

631. Burnley
632. The Conference League Cup and the Setanta Shield
633. Yeovil Town
634. 4-1
635. 1989/90
636. Drinkwise
637. Bromsgrove Rovers
638. Spalding
639. Kidderminster Harriers
640. Northwich Victoria

DANNY WHITAKER

641. Wilmslow
642. Midfielder
643. 10
644. Oldham Athletic
645. 156 (15)
646. Bristol Rovers
647. 'Skull'
648. 23
649. Port Vale
650. 2005/06

KYLE LIGHTBOURNE

651. 1968
652. Walsall
653. 73: 61 (12)
654. Swansea City
655. Lavince

656. **Bermuda**

657. **Shrewsbury Town**

658. **Gil Prescott**

659. **14**

660. **Stoke City**

GRAEME TOMLINSON

661. **Watford**

662. **Striker**

663. **Murdoch**

664. **Stoke City**

665. **22 (24)**

666. **Bradford City**

667. **6**

668. **Cambridge United**

669. **Sammy McIlroy**

670. **Exeter City**

THE ASSOCIATE MEMBERS' CUP/THE FOOTBALL LEAGUE TROPHY

671. **Johnstone's Paint (The Johnstone's Paint Trophy)**

672. **1984/85**

673. **Tranmere Rovers**

674. **Wrexham**

675. **Middlesbrough**

676. **Danny Adams**

677. **AFC Bournemouth**

678. **Preston North End**

679. **Darlington**

680. **Rochdale**

KEVIN McINTYRE

681. **1977**

682. **Tranmere Rovers**

683. **Grimsby Town**

684. **Nationwide Conference Championship**

685. **16**

686. **Shrewsbury Town**

687. **Chester City**

688.   134
689.   Peterborough United
690.   Midfielder

DEREK KEVAN

691.   1968
692.   The Tank
693.   West Bromwich Albion
694.   8
695.   Bradford Park Avenue
696.   Sweden, 1958
697.   Chelsea
698.   Manchester City
699.   Peterborough United
700.   Luton Town

BEN SEDGEMORE

701.   Wolverhampton
702.   84 (18)
703.   £25,000
704.   Havant & Waterlooville
705.   6
706.   False: he is on the Management Committee of the Professional Footballers' Association
707.   Birmingham City
708.   Lincoln City
709.   Shrewsbury Town
710.   Midfielder

MICHAEL WELCH

711.   Irish
712.   Barnsley
713.   Defender
714.   1982
715.   Accrington Stanley
716.   5
717.   Hull City
718.   Bury

719. Gil Prescott

720. True

POSITIONS THEY PLAYED – 2

721.	Tony Waiters	Goalkeeper
722.	Brian Fidler	Centre forward
723.	Dennis Fidler	Winger
724.	Jamie Tolley	Midfielder
725.	Rae Ingram	Full back
726.	Ian Elsby	Right back
727.	Lennie Butt	Inside Right
728.	Wilf Hall	Goalkeeper
729.	Sean Hessey	Defender
730.	Dave Roberts	Wing Half

THE SWINGING 60s

731. Roger Wood

732. Frank Bowyer

733. Tottenham Hotspur

734. The Cheshire Senior Cup (1960, 1964 and 1969)

735. Northwich Victoria (1964 and 1969) and Hyde United (1960)

736. Fulham

737. Wigan Athletic

738. The Cheshire League Challenge Cup

739. 1961, 1964 and 1968

740. 1960/61

PLAYING YEARS AT THE CLUB – 2

741.	John Askey	1984-2003
742.	Ryan Price	1995-99
743.	Bill Myerscough	1966-67
744.	Kieron Durkan	1998-2001
745.	Paul Harsley	2004-06
746.	Wilf Hall	1963-72
747.	John Miles	2002-07
748.	Martin Clark	1995-96
749.	Efe Sodje	1997-99
750.	David Morley	2005-07

THE GLAM SLAM 70s

751.   2
752.   1971 and 1973
753.   Inter-Town Football Cup
754.   Buxton
755.   The FA Challenge Trophy
756.   Telford United
757.   1970
758.   The Silkgirls
759.   The rear stanchions of the net, which caused the goals to collapse
760.   Kevin Keegan

MATCH THE YEAR – 3

761.   2001
762.   1963
763.   1966
764.   1968
765.   1951
766.   1994
767.   1980
768.   1999
769.   1981
770.   1971

THE NEW ROMANCE 80s

771.   Dave Sexton
772.   1 (1983)
773.   1988 and 1989
774.   1987
775.   1 (1985)
776.   Worcester City
777.   Runcorn
778.   Steve Burr and Stewart Chapman
779.   Brian Booth
780.   1987/88

NON-LEAGUE MANAGERS

781.	Peter Wragg	1986-93
782.	John Collins (player/manager)	1975-76
783.	Albert Leake (player/manager)	1963-67
784.	William Edwards (player/manager)	1947-49
785.	Brian Booth	1981-85
786.	Dave Connor	1976-78
787.	Frank Beaumont (player/manager)	1968-72
788.	James Stevenson	1936-37
789.	Bert Swindells	1955-58
790.	Phil Staley	1978-80

POT LUCK

791.	Maidstone United (won 1-0)
792.	Steve Burr
793.	The Staffordshire Senior Cup
794.	11
795.	Stephen Morris
796.	Kristian Dennis
797.	Altrincham
798.	2007/08
799.	Germany
800.	Dwayne Johnson aka 'The Rock'

NOTES

NOTES

NOTES

NOTES

NOTES

NOTES

NOTES

NOTES

NOTES

www.apexpublishing.co.uk